CREATE YOUR OWN
MASTERPIECE

Follow us on social media!

Tag us and use #piccadillyinc in your posts
for a chance to win monthly prizes!

© 2017 Piccadilly (USA) Inc.

This edition published by Piccadilly (USA) Inc.

Piccadilly (USA) Inc.
12702 Via Cortina, Suite 203
Del Mar, CA 92014
USA

10 9 8 7 6 5 4 3 2 1

Printed in China

ISBN-13: 978-1-62009-697-0

CREATE YOUR OWN
MASTERPIECE

With this book, you can create forty masterpieces of your own, drawing inspiration from the great masters of the art world. Every piece of art in this book is paired with an artistic prompt connected to the piece it accompanies. Who do you want to see emerging from Venus' seashell? In what modern city would your American Gothic be set? Follow the instructions, but most importantly, have fun expressing your creativity. We've even set you up with light tracing lines to get you started.

Did you ever wonder what it means to be an Impressionist—a Cubist, even? Then spend some time exploring the technique of the men and women who launched movements. Delve into the realistic and the abstract alike, learn by imitating, and travel back in time through the many ages of classic art.

Are you ready to impress your friends at art museums? This book will develop your artistic skills and your knowledge of art history and technique at the same time. Not only do you get to channel you inner Rembrandt, you also gain a nugget of wisdom about his life, work and influence, as each iconic piece of art includes a short biography of the artist.

Remember, these artists are famous because they defied and built upon convention to capture their unique vision. We hope this book is a first step toward yours.

Piccadilly
WWW.PICCADILLYINC.COM

VINCENT VAN GOGH

Café Terrace at Night, 1888, Oil on canvas
Kröller-Müller Museum, Otterlo

Vincent Van Gogh is one of the western world's most recognizable artists, and is certainly the most famous artist from the Netherlands. His work represents the Post-Impressionist movement, which is famous for its use of vibrant shapes and colors. Post-Impressionism arose in response to the Impressionists' fixation with capturing natural light and color. *Cafe Terrace at Night*, as well as his most well-known painting *The Starry Night*, is part of Van Gogh's nocturne series and was the first of his paintings to feature a starry sky.

VINCENT VAN GOGH

Draw a night scene at a cafe, inspired by Vincent Van Gogh's nocturne series.

HENRI MATISSE

The Green Stripe (La Raie Verte), 1905, Oil on canvas
Statens Museum for Kunst, Copenhagen

Henri-Émile-Benoît Matisse was a French artist who experimented in many forms of media and many styles. He was a painter, but he also specialized in printmaking, drafting and sculpting. Matisse's body of work includes paintings in keeping with Modernism and Post-Impressionism, but he is best known for his Fauvist work (Fauvist is French for "wild beasts"). The heavy brush strokes and strong colors in *The Green Stripe,* also known as *Portrait of Madame Matisse,* make it a distinctly Fauvist piece.

Recreate the portrait by Henri Matisse, using a different color palette.

PAUL GAUGUIN

Te as no areois (The Seed of the Areoi), 1892, Oil on burlap
Museum of Modern Art

Paul Gauguin was a French artist who strayed from conventional French society. Even though he was trained in Impressionism, he later left the movement to cultivate his own new style called Symbolism. Gauguin's most famous work is inspired by the culture and bright colors of French Polynesia, where the artist started a new life away from western culture. Paintings like *Te as no areois* show how Gauguin blended the western style and technique of his early years with his preferred non-western subject matter.

Draw yourself in a scene of an island getaway, influenced by
Paul Gauguin's French Polynesia inspired works.

CLAUDE MONET

Sunrise (Marine). March or April 1873, Oil on canvas
The J. Paul Getty Museum, Los Angeles

Impression, Sunrise, 1872 Oil on canvas
Musée Marmottan Monet, Paris

Oscar Claude Monet is credited with being the first French Impressionist. His devotion to plein-air painting and his focus on capturing the essence of natural light defined the form. In fact, this painting, *Impression, Sunrise*, first shown in 1874, is thought to have given the movement its name.

Create a seaside masterpiece inspired by Claude Monet.

EDGAR DEGAS

Dancers at the Bar. 1888, Mixed Media on Canvas
The Phillips Collection, Washington, DC

If you see an Impressionist painting or sculpture of a ballet dancer, chances are it is the work of Edgar Degas. A French artist, sculptor and draftsman, Degas devoted more than half of his artistic endeavors to ballet and ballet dancers. While painting *Dancers at the Bar*, Degas impulsively repositioned the dancers' arms and legs to mimic the strict and repetitive movements of a ballet rehearsal.

Create your own masterpiece using the Impressionist
style Degas uses in *Dancers at the Bar.*

The Kiss, 1907-1908, Oil on canvas
Österreichische Galerie Belvedere, Vienna

Gustav Klimt, an Austrian Symbolist painter, was a founding member of the Vienna Secession of 1897. Klimt and his fellow Austrian artists, as well as architects and sculptors, provided a platform for young upcoming artists to show their work. In what is known as his "Golden Phase," Klimt fused the styles of Art Nouveau with the Arts & Crafts movement. The intricate line work of the cloak and the gold leaf he used to accentuate and provide texture to the overall piece shows this melding of styles.

Create a wall tapestry using an Art Nouveau pattern inspired by Gustav Kllimt.

WASSILY KANDINSKY

Points,. 1920, Oil on canvas
Ohara Museum of Art, Kurashiki, Japan

Wassily Kandinsky began his artistic studies in his thirties and was a pioneer of the abstract modern art movement. He was also a master of Bauhaus, which delved into the relationship between art and function. Kandinsky believed in expressing spirituality in his art and wrote extensive theoretical works on this subject, including *The Blue Rider Almanac* and *On the Spiritual In Art*. His painting entitled *Points* highlights his *Point and Line to Plane* theory. This analysis explores how geographical elements work together to give the viewer a non-objective, intuitive message.

Create your own masterpiece using Kandinsky's *Point and Line to Plane* theory.

HOKUSAI

The Great Wave off Kanagawa, 1829-1832, Woodblock print
Metropolitan Museum of Art, New York

Katsushika Hokusai created the wave known around the world, *The Great Wave off Kanagawa*, as a part of his *Thirty-six Views of Mount Fuji* series. A Japanese artist, painter and printmaker of the Edo period, Hokusai specialized in ukiyo-e, the woodblock printing process in which white areas are chiseled away from the wood and the image or characters are left behind to be stamped, rubbed or printed onto the page.

Create your own *"The Great Wave"* inspired by
Hokusai's wood block printing technique.

The Old Guitarist. 1903, Oil on panel
The Art Institute of Chicago and jacquelinemhadel.com

Pablo Picasso, born Pablo Ruiz y Picasso, was a Spanish artist of all trades, though he spent most of his life in France. This painter, printmaker, sculptor, stage designer, ceramicist, poet and playwright is respected as one of the best and most influential artists of the 20th century. Picasso co-founded the Cubist movement, which followed his famous Rose and Blue periods. *The Old Guitarist* is an example of his Blue period, featuring paintings done mainly in shades of blue and blue-green, with muted and melancholy subject matter.

Draw a monochromatic musical piece inspired by Pablo Picasso.
What color are you feeling today?

Divan Japonais, 1892–1893, Lithograph printed in four colors, wove paper

Toulouse-Lautrec joins Cézanne, Van Gogh and Gauguin as one of the best-known Post-Impressionists. Known in his own time and beyond as an aristocrat, a dwarf, and a lush who loved to party, Toulouse-Lautrec elevated advertising to the realm of fine art. His legendary design of the Moulin Rouge posters are the most well-known examples of this practice. He created the lithograph poster, *Divan Japonais* to advertise a café-chantant of the same name.

HENRI DE TOULOUSE-LAUTREC

Design an advertisement for a local cafe in the style of Toulouse-Lautrec.

GEORGES SEURAT

Georges-Pierre Seurat is an icon of French 19th-century art. The first Neo-Impressionist painter, Seurat innovated the use of drawing media and invented the techniques known as chromoluminarism and pointillism, which used tiny dots of multi-colored paint to give the optical effect of blending. His large-scale painting, *A Sunday Afternoon on the Island of La Grande Jatte* (1884–1886), changed the direction of modern art because it showed members of every social class enjoying the park at the same time.

GEORGES SEURAT

Create a scene by the lake using the same pointillism technique Seurat uses in *A Sunday Afternoon on the Island of La Grande Jatte.*

PAUL CÉZANNE

Still Life with a Curtain,. 1898, Oil on canvas
Hermitage Museum, Saint Petersburg

Paul Cézanne was a French artist who helped to transition late 19th-century Post-Impressionism to early 20th-century Cubism. In fact, Matisse and Picasso called him "the father of us all." Cézanne is easily recognized by his characteristic repetitive, exploratory brushstrokes. He studied his subjects with intensity and used planes of color and small brushstrokes to build up and form complex fields. *Still Life with a Curtain* is known as Cézanne's greatest still life because of its dynamic composition, resonant light, and balance of form and color.

PAUL CÉZANNE

Create a still life composed of things you find around your house in the same Post-Impressionist style used by Paul Cézanne.

PIET MONDRIAN

Composition with Red, Blue, and Yellow, 1930, Oil on canvas
Kunsthaus Zürich, Switzerland

Piet Mondrian was a Dutch painter who developed a non-representational form called neoplasticism. He also contributed to the De Stijl art movement originated by Theo van Doesburg, an example of which is Mondrian's most famous painting, *Composition with Red, Blue, and Yellow*. The De Stijl style consists of a white background beneath a grid of vertical and horizontal black lines and the three primary colors.

PIET MONDRIAN

Connect the dots to create a grid of horizontal and vertical lines. Fill in the blank spaces with the color red, blue or yellow to create your very own Piet Mondrian inspired masterpiece!

EDVARD MUNCH

The Scream, 1893, oil, tempera & pastel on cardboard
National Gallery, Norway

Edvard Munch was a painter and printmaker from Norway. His haunting use of psychological motifs evolved some of the main traditions of late 19th-century Symbolism and influenced early 20th century German Expressionism. *The Scream* is by far Munch's most well-known work and is one of the world's most recognizable and provocative paintings. Munch used broad bands of clashing colors, a high viewpoint, and over-simplified forms to reduce the agonized figure to a warped skull that is clearly in the midst of an emotional crisis. This work is thought to represent the widespread anxiety of modern man.

EDVARD MUNCH

Create a portrait of yourself in the style of Edvard Munch's *The Scream* using the template below.

PIERRE-AUGUSTE RENOIR

Luncheon of the Boating Party, 1881, Oil on canvas
The Phillips Collection, Washington, D.C.

The French painter Pierre-Auguste Renoir, commonly known as Auguste Renoir, is remembered as one of the main developers of the Impressionist style. He revered beauty and feminine sensuality in his subjects, and it has been said that "Renoir is the final representative of a tradition which runs directly from Rubens to Watteau." *Luncheon of the Boating Party* is recognized as one of Renoir's best works as it shows his rich forms, fluid brush strokes, and captures lively, flickering light.

Finish the image below of a man in a boating hat in the Impressionist style of Renoir, using the same techniques used in *Luncheon of the Boating Party*.

AMEDEO MODIGLIANI

Head of a Woman,. 1910-11, Limestone
National Gallery of Art, Washington D.C.

Amedeo Clemente Modigliani was an Italian Jewish painter and sculptor known for his portraits and nudes. His characteristic use of modern, elongated faces and figures was not well-received in his lifetime. Though he worked mainly in France, he drew inspiration from African and Pre-Colombian statuary. *Head of a Woman* is a perfect example of his signature style. Modigliani embraced quirks and asymmetries, and though his work is largely figurative, it is also highly expressive. Eventually, he shifted his focus to concentrate on sculpting.

AMEDEO MODIGLIANI

Create a sculpture rendering of a head with an elongated face and abstract features like Modigliani's *Head of a Woman*.

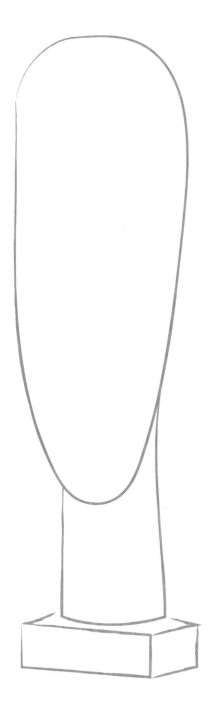

MARY CASSATT

The Boating Party, 1893-1894, Oil on canvas
National Gallery of Art, Washington

Mary Cassatt was a painter and printmaker born in Pennsylvania. Her art showed the private and social lives of women, especially the relationship between mothers and children. Though she was an American, she spent most of her adult life in France. There she met and befriended Edgar Degas and her work was shown alongside the Impressionists. Her connections back in the States also enabled her to bring French avant-garde painting to this country. Cassatt also drew influence from the Japanese prints popular in Paris in the late 1800s. Their simplified color, bold composition, flat, patterned surfaces, and unusual angles show in her work. *The Boating Party* was one of her most lauded pieces because of its bold geometry and ornamental patterning of the surface.

Recreate *The Boating Party* and replace the woman and child with someone of your choosing. Incorporate the bold geometry, decorative patterning and simplified color as seen in the original.

Red Balloon, 1922, Oil on chalk-primed gauze, mounted on board
Solomon R. Guggenheim Museum, New York

Paul Klee, a Swiss-German artist, crafted his individual style with influences from Expressionism, Cubism, and Surrealism. His work shows great personality and musicality and is often playful and humorous. Klee taught at the Bauhaus school of art, design and architecture alongside Wassily Kandinsky. In *Red Balloon*, the viewer can see a charming cityscape disguised in a group of delicately colored, ethereal geometric shapes.

Connect the dots to create a geometric cityscape inspired by Paul Klee's *Red Balloon*.

LEONARDO DA VINCI

Mona Lisa, 1503-1506, oil on poplar wood
Musée du Louvre, Paris

Leonardo da Vinci—where to begin? Da Vinci was an Italian humanist painter and sculptor of the Renaissance period, but he was also the first recorded over-achiever. He explored architecture, science, music, mathematics, engineering, literature, anatomy, geology, astronomy, botany, history, and cartography, and contributed to the invention of the parachute, helicopter and tank. With that record, it's no surprise that he created the most famous painting in the world, the seemingly humble *Mona Lisa* or *"la Gioconda,"* the laughing one. Mona Lisa's subtle and mysterious smile has brought her worldwide renown.

LEONARDO DA VINCI

Create portrait of someone you know with a mysterious smile
and make your own *Mona Lisa* masterpiece!

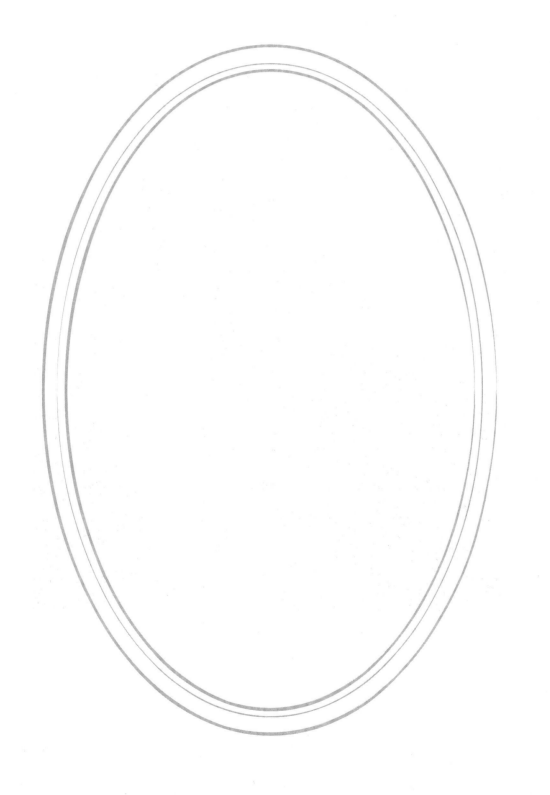

GRANT WOOD

American Gothic, 1930, Oil on beaverboard
Art Institute of Chicago

Grant DeVolson Wood is famous for his depictions of the rural American Midwest. The models in his iconic painting, *American Gothic*, were his sister, Nan Wood Graham and his dentist, Dr. Byron McKeeby. This painting is part of the American Regionalist movement, which included realist works depicting rural and small-town America, mostly in the Midwest and Deep South. The clothing, apron and pitchfork evoke 19th-century Americana. Wood used the same plants in the background of this painting as he did in his 1929 portrait of his mother entitled *Woman with Plants*.

GRANT WOOD

Create a modern day *American Gothic* using the template below. Notice the city background and updated clothing. Instead of the pitchfork used in the original painting, what other item can used to represent the current times?

Girl with a Pearl Earring, 1665, Oil on canvas
Mauritshuis, The Hague, Netherlands

Johannes Vermeer was a Dutch painter from the Dutch Golden Age and Baroque art movements. Vermeer depicted domestic indoor scenes of middle-class life. His best known painting, *Girl with a Pearl Earring*, is a "tronie," which is the 17th-century Dutch term for a painting of a head that isn't meant to be a portrait. This work in turn inspired a historical novel of the same name by Tracy Chevalier and was adapted into a film starring Scarlet Johansson as Griet, the girl with the pearl earring.

Design a series of earrings in the Baroque style.

SANDRO BOTTICELLI

Birth of Venus, 1486, Tempera on canvas
Uffizi, Florence

Sandro Botticelli, born Alessandro di Mariano di Vanni Filipepi, was a painter of the early Italian Renaissance period, characterized as a "golden age" by Giorgio Vasari. Botticelli was part of the Florentine School under the patronage of Lorenzo de' Medici. The Medici family commissioned much of his work, including his most famous works, *The Birth of Venus* and *Primavera*. *The Birth of Venus* is continual subject of study for art historians, who seek out interpretations and sources for Botticelli's imagery. Ernst Gombrich's theory that the painting represents the Neoplatonic idea of divine love in the nude form of Venus is the most enduring interpretation.

SANDRO BOTTICELLI

In the shell below, replace Venus with your idea of divine love.
It can be whoever or whatever comes to mind!

ÉDOUARD MANET

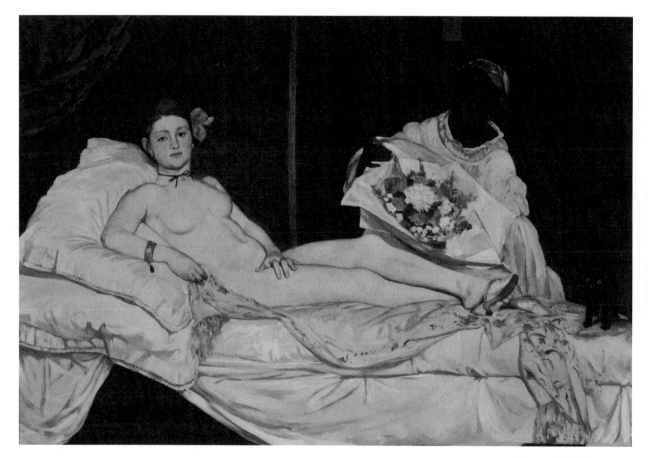

Olympia, 1863, Oil on canvas
Musée d'Orsay, Paris

Édouard Manet was a French painter whose portrayal of 19th-century modern life made him a bridge between the Realist and Impressionist movements. While they are now considered watershed paintings that marked the birth of modern art, his two 1863 masterpieces, *The Luncheon on the Grass* and *Olympia*, were very controversial in their time and inspired the young painters who would eventually create Impressionism. *Olympia*, exhibited at the 1865 Paris Salon, depicts a nude white woman lying on a bed receiving flowers from a black servant. Because she is thought to be a prostitute, Olympia and her direct gaze caused quite a shock when the painting was first exhibited.

Draw a reclining nude in the chaise lounge below in the same style as Édouard Manet's *Olympia*.

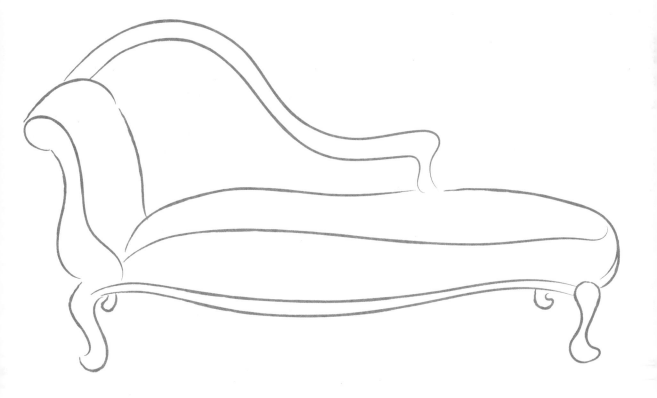

HIERONYMUS BOSCH

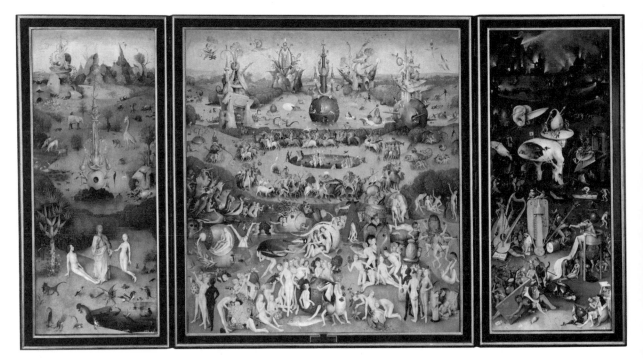

The Garden of Earthly Delights,c. 1495–1505, Oil on panel
Museo del Prado in Madrid

Hieronymus Bosch was a Dutch painter and draftsman from Brabant. One of the most prominent representatives of Early Netherlandish painting school, Bosch's work is famous for its fantastic imagery, detailed backgrounds, and often macabre depictions of religious narratives. His style and nightmarish illustrations of hell were widely copied by his peers.

His most impressive surviving work is a triptych called *The Garden of Earthly Delights*. This masterwork is painted in oil on three oak panels that close in like shutters. When folded, the outer wings show a painting of the Creation done in grisaille, or greyscale. When opened, the three scenes of the inner panels are believed to be intended to tell a story chronologically from left to right. On the left panel, God presents Eve to Adam, the center shows a detailed panorama of nude figures interacting with each other, fantastical animals, unnaturally large fruit and stone formations. The hellscape on the far-right panel portrays the torture of damnation.

HIERONYMUS BOSCH

Create a triptych of the story of your life. The first panel will reflect your past, the second panel will reflect your present and the third panel will reflect your future.

HENRI ROUSSEAU

The Sleeping Gypsy, 1897, Color on canvas
Museum of Modern Art, NY

Henri Julien Félix Rousseau was a French Post-Impressionist artist in the Naïve or Primitive style. He was jokingly referred to as *Le Douanier*, the customs officer, because he earned a living as a toll collector. Though he is respected today as a highly skilled, self-taught genius whose work influenced generations of avant-garde painters, critics ridiculed him in his lifetime.

Rousseau's painting, *The Sleeping Gypsy*, depicts a pensive lion standing over a sleeping gypsy woman. According to Rousseau this painting shows, "A wandering Negress, a mandolin player, lies with her jar beside her (a vase with drinking water), overcome by fatigue in a deep sleep. A lion chances to pass by, picks up her scent yet does not devour her. There is a moonlight effect, very poetic."

Recreate *The Sleeping Gypsy* in the scene below.
Instead of a lion, use an animal that has significant meaning to you.

EGON SCHIELE

Self-Portrait with Physalis, 1912, Color on canvas
Museum of Modern Art, NY

Egon Schiele was a 20th-century Austrian painter and a pupil of Gustav Klimt. His largely figurative work is characteristically intense and doesn't shy away from raw sexuality, even in his many (sometimes nude) self-portraits. Schiele is an early representative of the Expressionist movement, shown in the expressive lines and twisted body shapes of his paintings and drawings.

Schiele painted *Self-Portrait with Physalis* at the age of 22. The simultaneously confident and fragile style captivates the viewer, while his composition is expertly balanced. No line is without a counterpart, and the hair and body are both cropped to somewhat reflect each other. The positioning of the shoulders is intriguing to the eye, and the figure is counterbalanced by the slender branches of the red lampion fruit.

Create your own *"Self-Portrait with Physalis"* below in the Expressionist style of Egon Schiele.

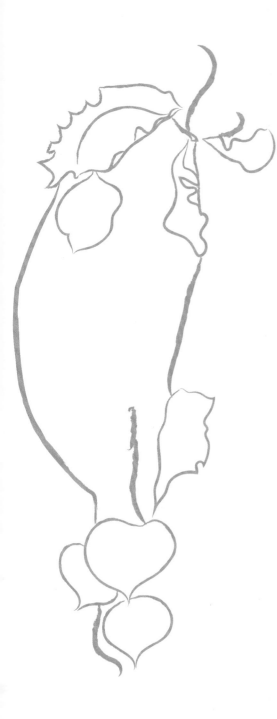

FERNAND LÉGER

Soldier with a Pipe, 1916, Oil on canvas
Kunstsammlung Nordrhein-Westfalen, Düsseldorf

Joseph Fernand Henri Léger was a French painter, filmmaker, and sculptor. Early in his artistic career, he began with a personal form of Cubism upon which he developed into a more figurative, populist style. His bold yet simple depictions of modern subjects has earned him a reputation as a forerunner of pop art.

Léger's service during World War I had a huge impact on his art. He spent two years at the front in Argonne in the French Army, where he drew many sketches of artillery, airplanes, and his fellow soldiers in the trenches. He painted *Soldier with a Pipe* (1916) when he was on furlough.

Create a geometric landscape inspired by Fernand Léger's Cubist style.

FRANZ MARC

Blue Horses, 1911, Oil on canvas
Walker Art Center, Minneapolis, Minnesota

Franz Marc was one of the major painters of the German Expressionist movement. He co-founded the art journal, *Der Blaue Reiter*, The Blue Rider, for which he and his collaborating artists were widely known.

Blue Horses is an early but major work in Marc's canon. He often painted animals, and this painting is the most important example in a series of portraits depicting horses in various colors. Marc considered animals divine, spiritual beings, purer and more beautiful than man.

Recreate Franz Marc's *Blue Horses* in your favorite color.

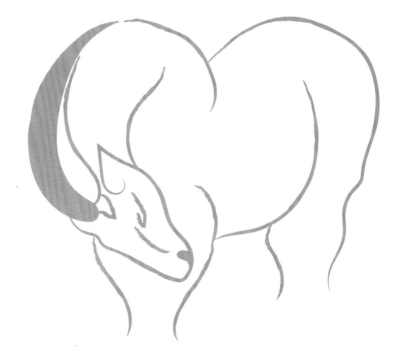

WILLIAM MORRIS

Design for St James's Palace, 1881, block printed in distemper colours, on paper

William Morris was an English translator, writer, socialist activist and textile designer of the British Arts and Crafts Movement. He played a major role in reviving traditional British textile arts and production methods.

Morris made a start at painting but eventually found that his work was devoid of movement. He decided to focus his efforts on designing wallpaper patterns instead and created the design above for the Grand Staircase in St. James's Palace.

Choose a color palette and color the design below to create your own William Morris wallpaper!

REMBRANDT

Christ in the Storm on the Lake of Galilee, 1633, Oil on canvas

Rembrandt Harmenszoon van Rijn was a 17th-century Dutch artist and is revered as a master draughtsman, painter, and printmaker during the Dutch Golden Age. He is, in fact, considered the most important visual artist in Dutch art history and one of the greatest artists in the history of art. Never nailed down to a characteristic theme, Rembrandt's body of work depicts a wide spectrum of style and subject matter, from landscapes, to portraits and self-portraits, animal studies, genre scenes, symbolic and historical scenes, and biblical and mythological themes.

Christ in the Storm on the Lake of Galilee is Rembrandt's only seascape. It portrays the fourth chapter of the Gospel of Mark in which Jesus calms the storm on the Sea of Galilee.

Using "Pandora's box" mythological theme, create a scene of epic porportions that rivals Rembrandts' *Christ in the Storm on the Lake of Galilee.*

La Grande Odalisque, 1814, Oil on canvas
Musée du Louvre

Jean-Auguste-Dominique Ingres was a French Neoclassical painter who is most widely recognized for his drawn and painted portraits. Though he preferred to think of himself as a painter of history after Nicolas Poussin and Jacques-Louis David, his favorite subject was the female nude. He often made imaginative changes to the female form with significant anatomical distortions. His most famous nude, *La Grande Odalisque*, shows a unique use of color, light and evocative tone.

Recreate *La Grande Odalisque* in a modern scene while still paying attention to use of color, lighting and tone as Ingres did in the original.

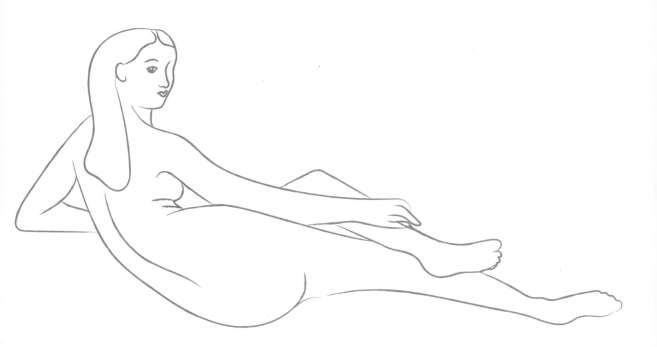

CARL LARSSON

Self-Portrait, 1906, Oil on canvas
Uffizi Gallery

Carl Larsson was a Swedish artist who loved to paint himself, often in a witty or causal manner. Larsson was a prolific representative of the Arts and Crafts Movement and painted oils, watercolors, and frescoes. In this *Self-Portrait*, a seemingly serious expression is humorously juxtaposed with a cross-eyed and expressive clown doll.

Recreate *Self Portrait* and add some humourous additions in Larsson's style, i.e. monocle, bowtie, corsage, clown nose. Have fun with it!

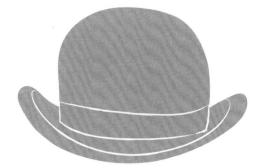

Portrait of Pablo Picasso, 1912, Oil on canvas
Art Institute of Chicago

Painter and sculptor, Juan Gris, born José Victoriano (Carmelo Carlos) González-Pérez in Madrid, Spain, spent most of his life living and working in France. Gris produced some of the most distinctive works of the Cubist movement. In the depiction of his mentor, *Portrait of Pablo Picasso*, Gris presents a larger-than-life Picasso with his palette in hand. In cool blue, gray and brown hues, Gris gives the illusion that all parts of the image are in motion. He does this by fracturing the image into a prism of planes and geometric shapes that visually blend with the parallel lines in the background.

Create a Cubism inspired self-portrait using the same techniques
Juan Gris used in *Portrait of Pablo Picasso*.

NATALIA GONCHAROVA

The Cyclist 1913, Oil on canvas
State Russian Museum

Natalia Sergeevna Goncharova was a Russian avant-garde painter, illustrator, writer, costume and set designer, and the wife of another leading Russian artist, Mikhail Larionov. Goncharova was a prominent member of the Donkey's Tail group, a collection of artists who spread the Cubo-Futurist movement in Russia. The text in her painting, *The Cyclist*, shows her interest in writing and graphic design. Goncharova also used multiple legs and feet in *The Cyclist* to convey the speed of an object in motion. The Futurist Manifesto supports her technique: "On account of the persistency of an image upon the retina, moving objects constantly multiply themselves; their form changes like rapid vibrations."

Create a graphic design using typography and convey movement by using the multiplication method as seen in *The Cyclist*.

Mavis perfume ad, 1920

Frederick Little Packer was an illustrator and political cartoonist born in Los Angeles, California. He attended the Los Angeles School of Art and Design and the Chicago Art Institute, and his art deco illustrations were featured in several publications. The image above, an advertisement for Mavis perfume, inspires feelings of sensuality and fantasy in women, its target audience. It plays up the product and at the same time minimizes any price points.

Create a perfume ad in the same style as Fred Parker's Mavis perfume ad.

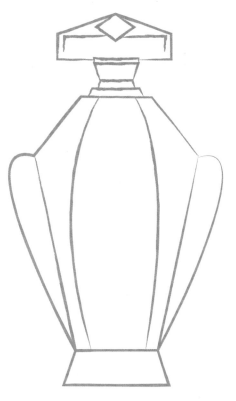

ALPHONSE MUCHA

Art nouveau poster of woman, advertising JOB cigarette papers.
Published in Paris by Imp. F. Champenois in 1898.

Alfons Maria Mucha, known as Alphonse Mucha, was a Czech Art Nouveau decorative artist and painter. He was a prolific creator of paintings, postcards, illustrations and advertisements, all done in his own distinct, signature style. Shown above, this Art Nouveau poster advertised JOB cigarette papers. While Mucha's commercial posters enjoyed a wide audience, he also produced work in a variety of other media, including jewelry, furniture and theatrical sets.

Create a Mucha inspired poster in the same Art Nouveau style seen in his JOB advertisements.

C.M. COOLIDGE

Poker Game, 1894, Oil on canvas

If you've seen a painting of dogs playing poker, you know Cassius Marcellus Coolidge. Coolidge was an American artist famous for creating an 18-piece series depicting anthropomorphized canines to advertise cigars. These images have become a staple of working-class home décor in the United States. The *Poker Game* was the first painting in the series done in 1894 and was sold at Sotheby's New York for $658,000 in November of 2015.

With inspiration from C.M. Coolidge's *Poker Game*, create four playing cards depicting anthropomorphized animals of your choosing.

JAMES WHISTLER

Arrangement in Grey and Black No. 1, 1871, Oil on canvas
Musée d'Orsay, Paris

James Abbott McNeill Whistler was an American artist mainly based in the UK. His art is part of the American Gilded Age. Known for being averse to sentimentality and moral suggestion in art, Whistler is one of the painters who contributed to the phrase "art for art's sake." His most famous painting, *Arrangement in Grey and Black No. 1*, is more commonly called *Whistler's Mother* and is an often-parodied portrayal of motherhood.

Recreate the *Arrangement in Grey and Black No.1* and surround the main subject with items you would find around your house today.

FRANCISCO GOYA

El Tres de Mayo 1808, 1814, Oil on canvas
Prado Museum

Greatly successful during his lifetime, the romantic painter and printmaker Francisco Goya is regarded as the most important Spanish artist of late 18th and early 19th centuries. His is considered a chronicler and interpreter of his time and also one of the best modern portraitists. Goya is often given double billing as one of the last of the Old Masters and the first of the moderns. This painting in particular, with its break from the traditions of war imagery and the Christian narrative, is said to mark the beginning of the modern era of painting.

In his *El Tres de Mayo 1808* (The Third of May 1808), Goya memorialized the Spanish resistance to Napoleon during the occupation of 1808 in the Peninsular War. Just looking at it on this small page, you can feel the emotional response Goya was so adept at evoking. This painting is deservedly a groundbreaking, standard bearing image of the horrors of war.

Design a poster around a social injustice issue that you are passionate about.

Las Meninas, 1656, Oil on canvas
Prado Museum

Diego Rodriguez de Silva y Velázquez was a Spanish painter of the contemporary Baroque period and the principal artist in the court of King Philip IV. Velázquez created many scenes of cultural and historical significance. His masterwork, *Las Meninas* is a culmination of the scores of portraits he painted of the Spanish royal family, other European figures of note, and commoners.

Las Meninas shows a room in the Royal Alcazar of Madrid during the reign of King Philip IV of Spain. In it, Infanta Margaret Theresa is in the midst of her entourage while behind them, Velázquez himself is portrayed painting a large canvas in the background. The painting features a candid scene of figures from the Spanish court in which some subjects look at the viewer and others engage among themselves. A mirror on the wall reflects the king and queen as if they are in the same position as the viewer, although some art historians believe that their image is a reflection from the painting Velázquez is crafting.

Recreate *Las Meninas* with you as Infanta Margaret Theresa surrounded by an entourage of your choosing.

PRACTICE PAGE

PRACTICE PAGE

PRACTICE PAGE

PRACTICE PAGE

PRACTICE PAGE

PRACTICE PAGE

PRACTICE PAGE

PRACTICE PAGE

PRACTICE PAGE

PRACTICE PAGE

PRACTICE PAGE

Looking for more?

Similar titles available by Piccadilly:

300 Drawing Prompts

500 Drawing Prompts

Complete This Drawing

Draw the Story

Sketching Made Easy

Calligraphy Made Easy

Calligraphy Made Easy: Project Book

Sketch THIS!

Rip it! Write it! Draw it!

300 Writing Prompts

500 Writing Prompts

Complete the Story

Write the Story

Write the Poem

Journal THIS!

The Story of My Life

My Ultimate Bucket List

My Top 10

WWW.PICCADILLYINC.COM